The Jacqueline Wilson Dream Journal

www.jacquelinewilson.co.uk

Also available by Jacqueline Wilson

Published in Corgi Pups, for beginner readers:
THE DINOSAUR'S PACKED LUNCH
THE MONSTER STORY-TELLER

Published in Young Corgi, for newly confident readers:
LIZZIE ZIPMOUTH
SLEEPOVERS

Available from Doubleday/Corgi Yearling Books:
BAD GIRLS
THE BED & BREAKFAST STAR
BEST FRIENDS
BURIED ALIVE!
THE CAT MUMMY
CLIFFHANGER
THE DARE GAME
DOUBLE ACT
GLUBBSLYME
THE ILLUSTRATED MUM
LOLA ROSE
THE LOTTIE PROJECT
MIDNIGHT
THE MUM-MINDER
SECRETS
THE STORY OF TRACY BEAKER
THE SUITCASE KID
VICKY ANGEL
THE WORRY WEBSITE

Available from Doubleday/Corgi Book, for older readers:
GIRLS IN LOVE
GIRLS UNDER PRESSURE
GIRLS OUT LATE
GIRLS IN TEARS
DUSTBIN BABY
LOVE LESSONS

The Jacqueline Wilson Dream Journal

Illustrated by
Nick Sharratt

CORGI YEARLING

THE JACQUELINE WILSON DREAM JOURNAL
A DOUBLEDAY BOOK 0 440 86708 8

Published in Great Britain by Doubleday,
an imprint of Random House Children's Books

Doubleday edition published 2005

This edition published exclusively for WH Smith

1 3 5 7 9 10 8 6 4 2

Doubleday Books are published by Random House Children's Books
61–63 Uxbridge Rd, London W5 5SA,
a division of The Random House Group Ltd,
in Australia by Random House Australia (Pty) Ltd,
20 Alfred Street, Milsons Point, Sydney, New South Wales 2061, Australia
in New Zealand by Random House New Zealand Ltd,
18 Poland Road, Glenfield, Auckland 10, New Zealand
and in South Africa by Random House (Pty) Ltd
Endulini, 5A Jubilee Road, Parktown 2193, South Africa

THE RANDOM HOUSE GROUP Limited No. 954009

www.**kids**at**randomhouse**.co.uk

A CIP catalogue record for this book is available from the British Library.

Printed and bound in Great Britain by Cox & Wyman Ltd, Reading, Berkshire

My Dreams

Children often ask me where I get my ideas from when I write my stories. I usually say that I don't really know how I do it. Ideas just seem to pop into my head. I say that it's a bit like when you dream. You can't really decide to have a dream. It just happens, whether you want it to or not. Sometimes it's a dream that seems very real, and it's a mixed-up version of something that's really happened. Sometimes it's completely bizarre and strange and magical and you have no idea how it floated into your head.

I wonder if you have vivid dreams? I find I have extraordinary dreams, but nowadays I have to write them down the moment I wake up or else they drift away in my thoughts and I can barely remember them.

I have such difficulty remembering the dreams I had last night and yet I can clearly remember some of the dreams I had as a child. I didn't sleep terribly well when I was little. I sometimes had the most awful nightmares. The worst kind were when people were chasing me and I'd think I'd woken up and was safe, but then they'd poke an arm through the wall and grab me out of my bed. I'd know that I was back in the nightmare and I'd try so hard to open my eyes to escape. That's one of the drawbacks of having an overactive imagination! However, I had beautiful childhood dreams too. I didn't often dream about flying but I had many weird and wonderful swimming dreams when I glided effortlessly along silvery rivers in the moonlight.

Do you think dreams ever come true? I don't think they necessarily do, but one or two of my recurring dreams do seem to have come true. I've dreamt about a big and beautiful house full of books on and off throughout my life – and now I'm actually living in that dream house. I also dreamt as a child that I was in some huge hall, standing on a stage, addressing a vast audience. It felt very strange and exciting. I couldn't believe so many people wanted to see and hear me. Whenever I give a talk about my books in a very big venue now, I remember that dream and smile.

I do hope you enjoy keeping this special journal. Sweet dreams!

Jacqueline Wilson

This Dream Journal belongs to

Name: ....

Address: ....

....

....

....

My star sign: ....

My passions: ....

....

....

My dislikes: ....

....

....

My appearance: ....

....

....

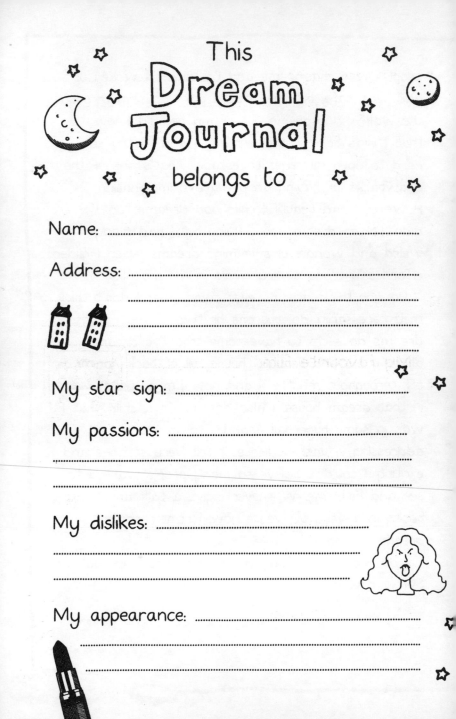

My best dream: ....

....

....

My worst nightmare: ....

....

....

My favourite book: ....

....

....

My favourite film: ....

....

....

My favourite music: ....

....

My ideal day: ....

....

....

My scariest night: ....

....

....

My Most Memorable Dreams

My Favourite Ever Dream

Date of dream ....

What happened in my dream ....

....

Mood of my dream ....

Main characters or symbols ....

....

Is it a recurring dream? ....

My Scariest Ever Dream

Date of dream ....

What happened in my dream ....

....

Mood of my dream ....

Main characters or symbols ....

....

Is it a recurring dream? ....

My Most Romantic Dream

Date of dream ....

What happened in my dream ....

....

Mood of my dream ....

Main characters or symbols ....

....

Is it a recurring dream? ....

My Weirdest Ever Dream

Date of dream ....

What happened in my dream ....

....

Mood of my dream ....

Main characters or symbols ....

....

Is it a recurring dream? ....

My Most Exciting Dream

Date of dream ....

What happened in my dream ....

....

Mood of my dream ....

Main characters or symbols ....

....

Is it a recurring dream? ....

My Dream with the Most Accurate Prediction

Date of dream ....

What happened in my dream ....

....

Mood of my dream ....

Main characters or symbols ....

....

Is it a recurring dream? ....

Dreams in Jacqueline Wilson's Books

Everybody has dreams. Often we don't remember them at all but sometimes they will be so vivid or shocking or lovely that they stay with us long after we've woken up.

Lots of the characters in Jacqueline's bestselling books have memorable dreams.
Here are some extracts from them:

Tracy's Dream
from *The Story of Tracy Beaker*

There wasn't much point in getting to sleep, because when I did eventually nod off I just had these stupid nightmares. It's as if there's a video inside my head and it switches itself on the minute my eyes close and I keep hoping it's going to be showing this great comedy that'll have me in stitches but then the creepy music starts and I know I'm in for it. Last night was the Great Horror Movie of all time. I was stuck in the dark somewhere and there was something really scary coming up quick behind me so I had to run like mad. Then I got to this big round pool and there were these stepping stones with people perching on them and I jumped on to the first one and there was no room at all because that fat Aunty Peggy was spread all over it. I tried to cling to her but she gave me a big smack and sent me flying. So then I jumped on to the next stepping stone and Julie and Ted were there and I tried to grab hold of them but they just turned their backs on me and didn't even try to catch me as I fell and so I had to try to reach the next stepping stone but

I was in the water doing my doggy-paddle and it was getting harder and harder, and every time I swam to a stepping stone all these people prodded at me with sticks and pushed me away and I kept going under the water and. . .

. . .and then I woke up and I know that whenever I dream about water it spells Trouble with a capital T. I had to make my own dash to the airing cupboard and the laundry basket. I was unfortunate enough to bump into Justine too. She didn't look as if she'd slept much either. Her eyes seemed a bit on the red side. I couldn't help feeling a bit mean then in spite of every-thing. So I gave her this big smile and said, 'I'm sorry about what happened to your alarm clock, Justine.'

Claire's Dream

from *The Worry Website*

I've had bad dreams before. I've dreamt I've been walking to school and suddenly I'm just wearing my knickers and everyone starts staring and pointing and giggling. I always feel silly going to school the next day, as if it had really happened!

I've also had a falling dream. I'm at the top of this very long escalator and I suddenly trip and I go tumbling down and down and down... until I wake up with a start.

Then there's that dream when I'm having a huge row with my sister Judy in our bedroom. She's bigger and bossier than me but I bash her with my pillow and she falls flat on her bed. She doesn't move. I think she's just pretending she's hurt to scare me, but my pillow feels strangely heavy and when I look inside I find it's full of rocks.

These are all pretty horrible dreams but they're not *too* bad. I don't think about them all the time.
I can make sure they don't really happen. I can check I'm wearing my school uniform, avoid all escalators, and stop bashing Judy with my pillow. Well, I *do* still have pillow fights with her but they're mostly in fun. I have a quick pummel of the pillow first to make sure it's totally rock-free.

But now I'm having this new nightmare. I dream it every night. It's awful.

I've tried getting into Judy's bed. She moaned and fussed and said I was squashing her. It didn't work anyway. I still had the nightmare. I woke up screaming. Judy woke up too.

'What are you playing at, Claire? You woke me up! Hey, are you crying?'

'No,' I sobbed.

'Yes, you are,' said Judy. She suddenly put her arms around me. 'Shall I get Mum?'

'*No!*'

This is the trouble. I can't tell Mum or Dad. They will say it's all my own fault. And I suppose it is.

You see I secretly watched this ultra-scary video. Mum and Dad are quite strict about what films we're allowed to see. Especially me. I don't know what's the matter with me. I've always been so stupid. When I was a really little kid I sometimes got scared watching *cartoons*! There's a bit where horses gallop wildly in *Beauty and the Beast* that made me have bad dreams. I used to wake up crying that the horses were after me. My big brother Michael used to neigh and make galloping noises just to get me going.

Mum got fed up getting up in the night so ever since she's been very picky over what I'm allowed to watch. I keep telling her and telling her that I wasn't a silly baby any more. I was furious when she let Michael and Judy watch *Titanic* but she wouldn't let *me*.

'Of course you can't watch it, Claire. You'd dream you were drowning and then you'd wet the bed,' Michael chortled.

I hated being left out. I knew silly old movies couldn't scare me any more. Or so I thought.

But then I watched *The Monster*. I wonder if you've seen it? It's been a *big* talking point in our school. Heaps of kids go on about how great it is and say it's the scariest film ever, ever, ever. Some kids say it didn't scare *them* one bit. But I think they're fibbing. I bet they haven't seen so much as the trailer.

Mandy's Dream

from *Bad Girls*

I started pretending. OK, I wasn't boring, baby,
goody-goody Mandy White any more. I was. . .
Miranda Rainbow. I was cool. I was colourful. I wore
loads of make-up and had this ultra-hip hairstyle.
I wore the most amazing super sexy clothes. I had
pierced ears and a stud in my nose. I didn't have
a mum. I didn't have a dad. I lived all by myself in
this incredible modern flat. Sometimes my friends
stayed overnight at my place. I had heaps of friends
and they all begged me to be their *best* friend.

   I fell asleep being Miranda Rainbow
but then Mum woke me up tucking
the covers over me and I couldn't
get back to sleep for ages.

My dreams in
January

Date of dream ....

Describe your dream here ....
....
....
....
....
....
....
....
....
....
....
....
....
....

What do you think your dream might mean?..

....

....

....

....

....

....

....

                                    ....

                                    ....

                                    ....

....

....

                                    ....

                                    ....

                                    ....

                                    ....

                                    ....

                                    ....

                                    ....

Drawing of my dream

Date of dream ....

Describe your dream here ....
....
....
....
....
....
....
....
....
....
....
....
....
....
....
....
....
....

Drawing of my dream

What do you think your dream might mean?...
....
....
....
....
....
....
....
....
....
....
....
....
....
....
....
....
....
....
....
....

Date of dream ....

Describe your dream here ....

....

....

....

....

....

....

....

....

....

....

....

....

....

....

....

....

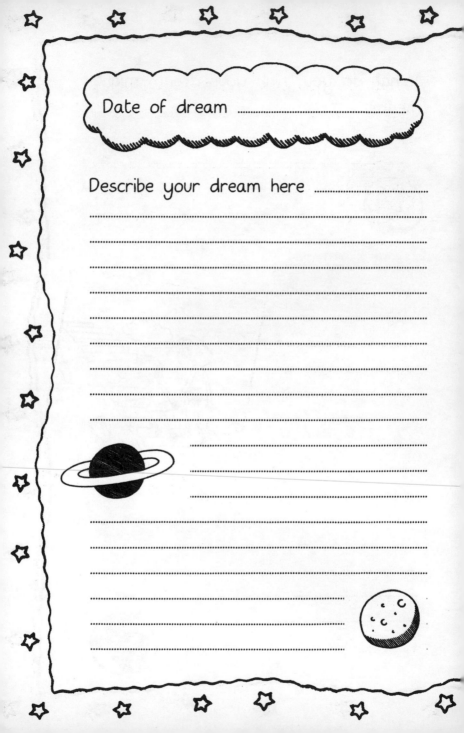

What do you think your dream might mean?...
....

....
....
....
....
....
....
....
....
....
....

....
....
....

Drawing of my dream

....
....
....
....
....
....

Date of dream ....

Describe your dream here ....

....

....

....

....

....

....

....

....

....

....

....

....

S is for Starlight

....

....

....

....

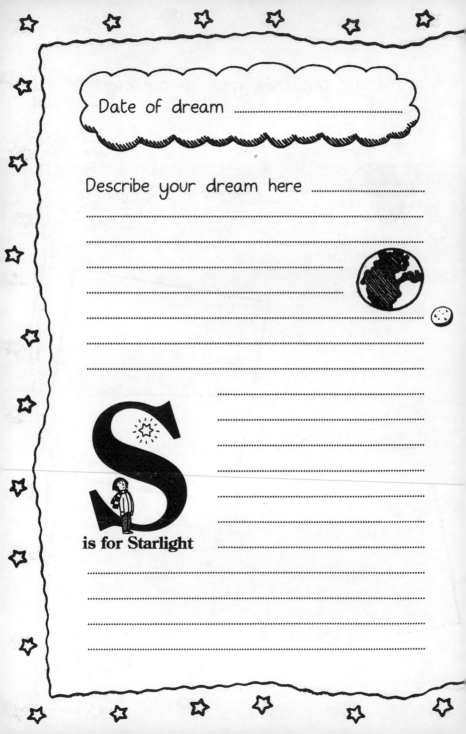

What do you think your dream might mean?..

....

....

....

....

....

....

....

....

....

....

....

....

....

....

....

....

....

Drawing of my dream

My dreams in February

Date of dream ....

Describe your dream here ....

....

....

....

....

....

....

....

....

....

....

....

....

What do you think your dream might mean?

....
....
....
....
....
....
....
....
....
....
....
....
....
....
....
....
....
....
....

Drawing of my dream

Date of dream ....

Describe your dream here ....

....

....

....

....

....

....

....

....

....

....

....

....

....

....

....

....

....

....

Drawing of my dream

What do you think your dream might mean?..

....

....

....

....

....

....

....

....

....

....

....

....

....

....

....

....

....

Date of dream ....

Describe your dream here ....

....

....

....

....

....

....

....

....

....

....

....

....

....

....

....

....

What do you think your dream might mean?..
....

....
....
....

....
....
....
....
....
....
....
....
....
....
....

....
....
....
....
....
....

Drawing of my dream

Date of dream ....

Describe your dream here ....

....

....

....

....

....

....

....

....

                                          ....

                                     ....

                              ....

                              ....

                              ....

....

....

....

....

What do you think your dream might mean?..

....

....

....

....

....

....

....

....

....

....

....

....

....

....

....

....

....

....

....

Drawing of my dream

My dreams in
March

Date of dream ....

Describe your dream here ....

....

....

....

....

....

....

....

....

....

....

....

....

What do you think your dream might mean?...

....

....

....

....

....

....

....

....

....

....

....

Drawing of my dream

Date of dream ....

Describe your dream here ....

....

....

....

....

....

....

....

....

                        ....

                        ....

                        ....

                        ....

                        ....

                        ....

                        ....

                        ....

Drawing of my dream   ....

What do you think your dream might mean?..
....
....

....
....
....
....
....
....
....

....
....
....
....
....
....
....
....

Date of dream ....

Describe your dream here ....

....

....

....

....

....

....

....

....

....

....

....

....

....

....

....

....

What do you think your dream might mean?...

Drawing of my dream

Date of dream ....

Describe your dream here ....
....
....
....
....
....
....
....
....
....
....
....
....
....
....
....
....
....

What do you think your dream might mean?..

....

....

....

....

....

....

....

....

....

....

....

....

....

....

....

....

....

....

....

Drawing of my dream

My dreams in
April

Date of dream ....

Describe your dream here ....
....
....
....
....
....
....
....
....
....
....
....
....
....

What do you think your dream might mean?...
....
....
....
....
....
....
....
                        ....
                        ....
                        ....
....
....
                                    ....
                                    ....
                                    ....
                                    ....
                                    ....
                                    ....
                                    ....

Drawing of my dream

Date of dream ....

Describe your dream here ....
....
....
....
....
....
....
....
....
                                    ....
                                    ....
                                    ....
                                    ....
                                    ....
                                    ....
                                    ....
                                    ....
                                    ....

Drawing of my dream

What do you think your dream might mean?

Date of dream ....

Describe your dream here ....

....

....

....

....

....

....

....

....

....

....

....

....

....

....

....

....

....

....

What do you think your dream might mean?..

....

....

....

....

....

....

....

....

....

....

....

Drawing of my dream

....

....

....

....

....

....

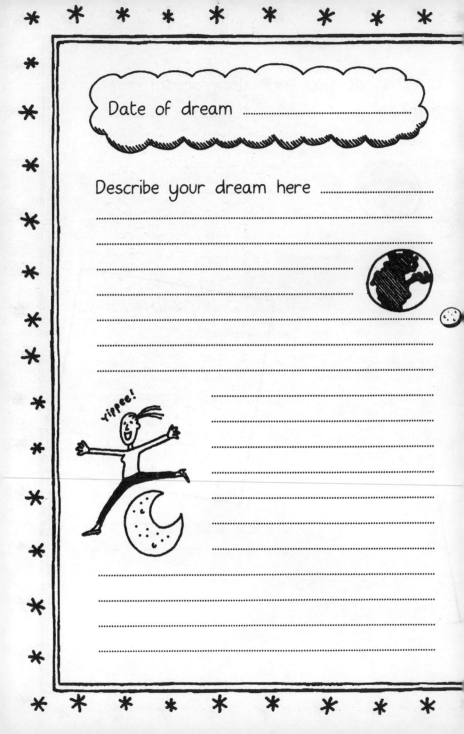

Date of dream ....

Describe your dream here ....
....
....
....
....
....
....
....
....
....
....
....
....
....
....
....
....
....

yippee!

What do you think your dream might mean?...

....

....

....

....

....

....

....

....

....

....

....

....

....

....

....

....

....

....

Drawing of my dream

My dreams in
May

Date of dream ....

Describe your dream here ....

....
....
....
....
....
....
....
....
....
....
....
....
....
....

What do you think your dream might mean?..

....

....

....

....

....

....

....

....

....

....

....

....

....

....

....

....

....

....

Drawing of my dream

Date of dream ....

Describe your dream here ....
....
....
....
....
....
....
....
....
....
....
....
....
....
....
....
....
....
....
....

Drawing of my dream

What do you think your dream might mean?..
....
....

....
....
....
....
....
....
....

....
....
....
....
....
....
....
....

Date of dream ....

Describe your dream here ....

....

....

....

....

....

....

....

....

....

....

....

....

....

....

....

....

....

....

What do you think your dream might mean?..

....

....

....

....

....

....

....

....

....

....

....

....

....

....

....

Drawing of my dream

....

....

....

....

....

Date of dream ....

Describe your dream here ....
....
....
....
....
....
....
....
....
....
....
....
....
....
....
....
....
....
....

What do you think your dream might mean?..
....
....
....
....
....
....
....
....
....
....
....
....
....
....
....
....
....
....

Drawing of my dream

My dreams in
June

Date of dream ....

Describe your dream here ....

....

....

....

....

....

....

....

....

....

....

....

....

....

....

What do you think your dream might mean?..

....

....

....

....

....

....

....

....

....

....

....

....

....

....

....

....

....

....

Drawing of my dream

Date of dream ....

Describe your dream here ....
....
....
....
....
....
....
....
....
....
....
....
....
....
....
....
....
....
....

Drawing of my dream

What do you think your dream might mean?...
....
....
....
....
....
....

....
....
....
....
....

....
....
....
....
....
....
....
....
....
....

Date of dream ....

Describe your dream here ....

....

....

....

....

....

....

....

....

....

....

....

....

....

....

....

....

....

....

What do you think your dream might mean?..

....

....

....

....

....

....

....

....

....

....

....

....

....

Drawing of my dream

....

....

....

....

....

Date of dream ....

Describe your dream here ....

....

....

....

....

....

....

....

....

....

....

....

....

....

....

....

....

....

What do you think your dream might mean?..
....
....
....
....
....
....
....
....
....
....
....
....
....
....
....
....
....

Drawing of my dream

My dreams in
July

Date of dream ....

Describe your dream here ....
....
....
....
....
....
....
....
....
....
....
....
....
....

What do you think your dream might mean?...
....
....
....
....
....
....
....
....
....
....
....
....
....
....
....
....
....
....
....
....

Drawing of my dream

Date of dream ....

Describe your dream here ....

....

....

....

....

....

....

....

....

....

....

....

....

....

....

....

Drawing of my dream

What do you think your dream might mean?..
....
....
....
....
....
....
....
....
....
....
....
....
....
....
....
....
....
....
....
....

Date of dream ....

Describe your dream here ....

....

....

....

....

....

....

....

....

....

....

....

....

....

....

....

What do you think your dream might mean?...

....

....

....

....

....

....

....

....

....

....

....

....

....

....

....

Drawing of my dream

....

....

....

....

....

....

Date of dream ....

Describe your dream here ....

....
....
....
....
....
....
....
....
....
....
....
....
....
....
....
....
....

What do you think your dream might mean?...

....

....

....

....

....

....

....

....

....

....

....

....

....

....

....

....

....

....

....

Drawing of my dream

My dreams in
August

Date of dream ....

Describe your dream here ....

....

....

....

....

....

....

....

....

....

....

....

....

....

What do you think your dream might mean?...
....
....
....
....
....
....
....

Drawing of my dream

Date of dream ....

Describe your dream here ....
....
....
....
....
....
....
....
....
....
....
....
....
....
....
....
....
....

Drawing of my dream

What do you think your dream might mean?..
....
....
....
....
....
....
....
....
....
....
....
....
....
....
....
....
....
....
....
....

Date of dream ....

Describe your dream here ....

....

....

....

....

....

....

....

....

....

....

....

....

....

....

....

....

What do you think your dream might mean?..

....

....

....

....

....

....

....

....

....

....

....

....

....

....

....

Drawing of my dream

....

....

....

....

....

....

Date of dream ....

Describe your dream here ....
....
....
....
....
....
....
....
....
....
....
....

....
....
....
....
....
....

What do you think your dream might mean?..
....
....
....
....
....
....
....
....
....
....
....
....
....
....
....
....
....
....
....
....

Drawing of my dream

Date of dream ....

Describe your dream here ....

....

....

....

....

....

....

....

....

....

....

....

....

....

....

....

....

....

....

What do you think your dream might mean?...
....
....
....
....
....
....

Drawing of my dream

....
....
....
....
....
....

My dreams in
September

Date of dream ....

Describe your dream here ....
....
....
....
....
....
....
....

....
....
....
....
....
....
....

What do you think your dream might mean?...
....
....
....
....
....
....
....
....
....
....
....
....
....
....
....
....
....
....

Drawing of my dream

Date of dream ....

Describe your dream here ....

....

....

....

....

....

....

....

....

....

....

....

....

....

....

....

....

....

Drawing of my dream

What do you think your dream might mean?

Date of dream ....

Describe your dream here ....
....
....
....
....
....
....
....
....
....
                          ....
                          ....
                          ....
....
....
....
....
....
....

What do you think your dream might mean?..
....
....
....
....
....
....
....
....
....
....
....
....
....
....
....

Drawing of my dream

....
....
....
....
....
....

Date of dream ....

Describe your dream here ....
....
....
....
....
....
....
....
....
....
....
....
....
....
....
....
....
....

What do you think your dream might mean?..
....
....
....
....
....
....
....
....
....
....
....
....
....
....
....
....
....
....

Drawing of my dream

Date of dream ....

Describe your dream here ....

....

....

....

....

....

....

....

....

....

....

....

....

....

....

....

What do you think your dream might mean?..
....
....
....
....
....
....
....

Drawing of my dream

....
....
....
....
....
....
....
....
....

....
....
....
....
....
....

My dreams in
October

Date of dream ....

Describe your dream here ....

....

....

....

....

....

....

....

....

....

....

....

....

....

What do you think your dream might mean?...

....

....

....

....

....

....

....

....

....

....

....

....

....

....

....

....

....

....

....

Drawing of my dream

Date of dream ....

Describe your dream here ....

....

....

....

....

....

....

....

....

....

....

....

....

....

....

....

Drawing of my dream

What do you think your dream might mean?..
....
....
....
....
....
....
....
....
....
....
....
....
....
....
....
....
....
....
....

Date of dream ....

Describe your dream here ....

....

....

....

....

....

....

....

....

....

....

....

....

....

....

....

....

What do you think your dream might mean?..
....
....
....
....
....
....
....
....
....
....
....
....
....

Drawing of my dream

....
....
....
....
....
....

Date of dream ....

Describe your dream here ....
....
....
....
....
....
....
....
....
....
....

....
....
....
....
....
....

What do you think your dream might mean?..

....

....

....

....

....

....

....

....

....

....

....

....

....

....

....

....

....

....

Drawing of my dream

Date of dream ....

Describe your dream here ....
....
....
....
....
....
....
....
....
....
....
....
....
....
....
....
....
....
....

What do you think your dream might mean?...
....
....
....
....
....
....
....

                                              ....
                                              ....
                                              ....
                                              ....
                                              ....
                                              ....
                                              ....
                                              ....
Drawing of my dream   ....

....
....
....
....
....
....

My dreams in
November

Date of dream ....

Describe your dream here ....

....

....

....

....

....

....

....

....

....

....

....

....

....

....

What do you think your dream might mean?...

....

....

....

....

....

....

....

....

....

....

....

....

....

....

....

....

....

....

....

Drawing of my dream

Date of dream ....

Describe your dream here ....

....

....

....

....

....

....

....

....

....

....

....

....

....

....

....

....

....

....

Drawing of my dream

What do you think your dream might mean?...
....
....
....
....
....
....
....
....
....
....
....
....
....
....
....
....
....
....
....

Date of dream ....

Describe your dream here ....

....

....

....

....

....

....

....

....

....

....

....

....

....

....

....

....

....

....

....

What do you think your dream might mean?...
....

....
....
....

....
....

....
....
....
....
....
....
....

Drawing of my dream

....
....
....
....
....
....

Date of dream ....

Describe your dream here ....
....
....
....
....
....
....
....
....
....
....

N
is for Night
....
....
....
....
....

What do you think your dream might mean?...
....
....
....
....
....
....
....
....
....
....
....

....
....
....
....
....
....
....

Drawing of my dream

Date of dream ....

Describe your dream here ....

....

....

....

....

....

....

....

....

....

....

....

....

....

....

....

....

What do you think your dream might mean?

....

....

....

....

....

....

```
Drawing of my dream
```

....

....

....

....

....

My dreams in

December

Date of dream ....

Describe your dream here ....

....

....

....

....

....

....

....

....

....

....

....

....

....

What do you think your dream might mean?..

....

....

....

....

....

....

....

....

....

....

....

....

....

....

....

....

....

....

....

Drawing of my dream

Date of dream ....

Describe your dream here ....

....

....

....

....

....

....

....

....

....

....

....

....

....

....

....

....

....

....

....

Drawing of my dream

What do you think your dream might
mean?...
....
....

....
....
....

....
....
....
....
....
....
....

....
....
....
....
....
....

....
....
....

Date of dream ....

Describe your dream here ....
....
....
....
....
....
....
....
....
....
....
....
....
....
....
....
....
....

What do you think your dream might mean?..

....

....

....

....

....

....

....

....

....

....

....

....

....

....

Drawing of my dream

....

....

....

....

....

....

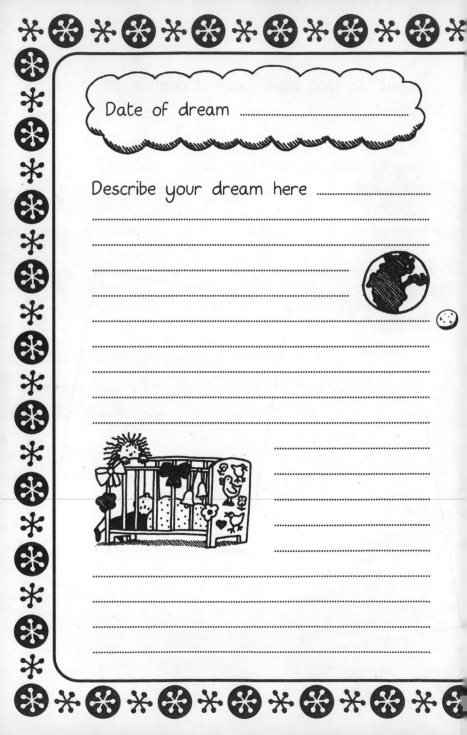

Date of dream ....

Describe your dream here ....

....

....

....

....

....

....

....

....

                          ....

                          ....

                          ....

                          ....

                          ....

....

....

....

....

What do you think your dream might mean?...
....
....
....
....
....
....
....
....
....
....
....
....
....
....
....
....
....
....
....

Drawing of my dream

Date of dream ....

Describe your dream here ....

....

....

....

....

....

....

....

....

....

....

....

....

....

....

....

....

What do you think your dream might mean?...
....
....
....
....
....
....
....
....
....
....
....
....
....
....
....
....
....
....

Drawing of my dream

About the Author

JACQUELINE WILSON was born in Bath in 1945, but has spent most of her life in Kingston-upon-Thames, Surrey. She always wanted to be a writer and wrote her first 'novel' when she was nine, filling countless Woolworths' exercise books as she grew up. She started work at a publishing company and then went on to work as a journalist on *Jackie* magazine (which was named after her) before turning to writing fiction full-time.

Since 1990 Jacqueline has written prolifically for children and has won many of the top awards for children's books, including the *Guardian* Children's Fiction Award, the Smarties Prize and the Children's Book of the Year. Jacqueline was awarded an OBE in the Queen's Birthday Honours list in 2002. She is the most borrowed author of all from British libraries and an astounding twenty million copies of her books have now been sold in the UK. As Children's Laureate in 2005-2007, she is a highly popular and respected figurehead for children's literature and reading in this country.

An avid reader herself, Jacqueline has a personal collection of many, many thousands of books. She has one grown-up daughter.

About the Illustrator

NICK SHARRATT knew from an early age that he wanted to use his artistic skills in his career. He went to Manchester Polytechnic to do an Art Foundation course, followed by a BA (Hons) in Graphic Design at St Martin's School of Art in London. Since graduating in 1984, Nick has been working full-time as an illustrator, with his work hugely in demand for children's books.

His famous collaboration with Jacqueline Wilson began with *The Story of Tracy Beaker*, published in 1991 and he has illustrated every one of her best-selling books published by Doubleday/Corgi since then.

Nick also illustrates full-colour picture and novelty books, such as *Eat Your Peas* (Bodley Head), written by Kes Gray, which won the 2000 Children's Book Award and *Pants* (David Fickling Books), written by Giles Andreae, which also won the Children's Book Award and was shortlisted for the prestigious Kate Greenaway Medal in 2003. He also writes his own picture books.

Nick lives in Brighton, Sussex.

CLEAN BREAK
Jacqueline Wilson

When Dad and Mum break up, Em does her best to cheer up her little brother and sister, even though she's miserable too. She dances around and tells wonderful tales all about their favourite glove puppet. Em knows how a good story can make life seem better. She is always cheered up by reading one of her favourite books. If Em got to meet the author, it would be a dream come true. But could her other greatest wish be granted? Is any story powerful enough to bring Dad back?

Another wonderful book about real family life from a prize-winning, best-selling author.

Doubleday

Join the FREE online

Jacqueline Wilson

✦ FAN CLUB ✦

Read Jacqueline's monthly diary, look up

tour info, receive fan club e-newsletters.

All this and more, including members'

jokes and loads of exclusive top offers

Visit www.jacquelinewilson.co.uk

for more info!